Meet the Mermaids

Written by Alexandra Robinson

Illustrated by Shannon Hays

make
believe
ideas

Letter to Parents

Dear Parents,

This book is an engaging early reader for your child. It combines simple words and sentences with delightful illustrations of mermaids. Here are some of the many ways you can help your child learn to read fluently.

Encourage your child to:
* Look at and explore the pictures.
* Sound out the letters in unknown words.
* Read and reread the text.

Look at the pictures
Make the most of each page by talking about the pictures and looking at the details together. Here are some questions you can use to discuss each page as you go along:
* Do you like this mermaid?
* What do you like about her?
* What is the mermaid doing here?
* Which mermaid would you like to meet? Why?

Look at rhymes
Many of the sentences in this book are simple rhymes. Encourage your child to recognize rhyming words. Try asking the following questions:
* What does this word say?
* Can you find a word that rhymes with it?
* Look at the endings of the rhyming words. Are they spelled the same? (Some are spelled the same, but not all. For example, "waves" and "caves," and "be" and "sea.")

Test understanding

It is one thing to understand the meaning of individual words, but you want to make sure that your child understands whole sentences and pages.

* Play "find the mistake." Read the text as your child looks at the words with you, but make an obvious mistake to see if he or she has understood. Ask your child to correct you and provide the right word.
* After reading the facts, close the book and make up questions to ask your child.
* Ask your child whether a fact is true or false.
* Provide your child with two or three answers to a question and ask her or him to pick the correct one.

Sight words

This page provides practice with commonly used words that children need to learn to recognize on sight. Not all of them can be sounded out. Familiarity with these words will increase your child's reading fluency.

Picture dictionary

This activity focuses on learning vocabulary relating to mermaids. All the words can be found in the book.

Make-believe quiz

This simple quiz will help you ascertain how well your child has understood and remembered the text. If your child cannot remember an answer, encourage him or her to look back in the book to find out.

Meet the Mermaids

Come and meet the mermaids.
They're friendly as can be.
They love to leap through ocean waves
and dive beneath the sea.

Did You Know?

The mermaids like to build underwater sandcastles.

5

Twinkly Tails

The mermaids swim with grace and speed
and swish their shiny tails.
They like to race their dolphin friends
and wander with the whales.

Did You Know?

Some mermaids' tails
change color to
match their mood.

Magical Music

They like to sing sweet melodies
and whistle with the birds.
They fill the air with soothing sounds
and whisper magic words.

Did You Know?

The mermaids can talk
to sea creatures.

little Mermaids

The little mermaids swim and play
in shallow seas and pools.
They practice flips and water tricks
at mermaid diving schools.

Did You Know?

At school, young mermaids learn to play magical golden harps.

Freshwater Mermaids

These mermaids live in mountain lakes
with turtles, fish, and frogs.
They like to splash in waterfalls
and rest on woodland logs.

Did You Know?
The freshwater mermaids
keep otters as pets.

Lagoon Mermaids

These mermaids swim in rocky coves
protected from big waves.
They look for precious jewels and gems
in secret, hidden caves.

Did You Know?
These mermaids use shells
and stones to make sand art.

Coral Mermaids

These mermaids live in coral reefs
where plants and creatures glow.
They glide with brightly colored fish
and help the corals grow.

Did You Know?

They use magic paints to
color the corals all sorts
of pretty shades.

Beach Mermaids

These mermaids live near sandy shores
and splash in shallow seas.
They love to make shell necklaces
and feel the ocean breeze.

Did You Know?

The beach mermaids use shell phones to talk to one another.

Royal Mermaids

The royal mermaids rule the sea
and wear gold coral crowns.
They live in pink pearl palaces
in underwater towns.

Did You Know?

The royal mermaids collect pearls from scallop shells.

Ice Mermaids

These mermaids swim in frozen seas and rest on icy floats.
They braid their hair with silver thread and wear warm winter coats.

Did You Know?
The ice mermaids sleep in underwater igloos beneath floating icebergs.

Deep-Sea Mermaids

The deep-sea mermaids swish and dive
down to the ocean floor.
They search for hidden treasure chests
and shipwrecks to explore.

Did You Know?
Their tails glow in the dark and bring light to the ocean depths.

Moonlight Mermaids

At night, these mermaids sit on rocks
enclosed in small lagoons.
They sing their gentle lullabies
and swim beneath the moon.

Did You Know?

These mermaids grant wishes made at sea and help dreams come true.

Sight Words

Here are some sight words used in context. Use other sight words from the border in simple sentences of your own.

The mermaids **can swim** and **dive**.

They have shiny tails.

I would love **to meet a** mermaid.

Picture Dictionary

Write the correct word under each picture
to create your own picture dictionary.

fish   shell   bird   mermaid   crown
sandcastle   dolphin   harp   moon

Make-Believe Quiz

How much do you know about mermaids?
Circle the answers to find out. If you
can't remember an answer, look back
in the book.

1

What do the mermaids
like to build underwater?

sandcastles   snowmen

2

What instruments do young
mermaids learn to play?

harps   flutes

3

Which animals whistle
with the mermaids?

frogs   birds

4

Where do coral mermaids live?

in coral reefs

in mountain lakes

5

What animals do freshwater mermaids keep as pets?

starfish   otters

6

Which mermaids grant wishes made at sea?

ice mermaids

moonlight mermaids

7

What do beach mermaids love to make?

shell necklaces   surfboards

Find Your Mermaid Name

Find the first letter of your name. The word next to it is the first part of your mermaid name.

A: River	**J:** Lavender	**S:** Pearl
B: Blue	**K:** Magic	**T:** Golden
C: Isla	**L:** Melody	**U:** Tropical
D: Coral	**M:** Aqua	**V:** Sandy
E: Crystal	**N:** Jewel	**W:** Dolphin
F: Luna	**O:** Maya	**X:** Lullaby
G: Silver	**P:** Waterlily	**Y:** Lake
H: Ocean	**Q:** Starfish	**Z:** Sea
I: Water	**R:** Moonlight	

Find the month you were born. The word next to it is the last part of your mermaid name.

January: Marine	**July:** Valley
February: Dancer	**August:** Shell
March: Sky	**September:** Icicle
April: Storm	**October:** Dream
May: Wave	**November:** Rain
June: Diamond	**December:** Song

Write your mermaid name here: